THE
UNEXPURGATED
MEMOIRS
OF
Bernard
Mergendeiler

Books by Jules Feiffer

Sick, Sick, Sick

Passionella

The Explainers

Boy, Girl. Boy, Girl.

Hold Me!

Harry, the Rat with Women

Feiffer's Album

*The Unexpurgated Memoirs
of Bernard Mergendeiler*

JULES FEIFFER

THE UNEXPURGATED MEMOIRS

OF

Bernard Mergendeiler

Random House   New York

INTRODUCTION

(The scene is a bedroom late at night. BERNARD *and* NAOMI *sit disconsolately)*

NAOMI   Don't feel too bad.

BERNARD   I'm sorry. You understand?

NAOMI   What's there to be sorry about?

BERNARD   I had too much to drink. You understand? I mean ordinarily I *never* have trouble like this.

NAOMI   Will you please believe me? You don't owe me any explanation. It's not as if it's a *test* or anything.

BERNARD   Well, it's when I have too much to drink you see —

NAOMI *(Trying to placate)*   What do you think—I *grade* men?

BERNARD *(Winces)*   It's the alcohol—I just can't *(Gropes for right word)* function—

NAOMI   Please, you needn't be so much on the *defensive.*

BERNARD *(Freezes)*   Who's on the defensive?

NAOMI   All I'm saying is it's not that much of a big—

BERNARD *(Tersely)*   Don't tell me I'm on the defensive when I'm not on the defensive.

NAOMI   Listen, I don't want to make a big thing out of—

BERNARD *(Bitterly)*   Yeah? Yeah? Yeah, I bet you don't, don't you? Yeah!

NAOMI   What's the matter with you?

BERNARD   Saying that I'm on the defensive *puts* me on the defensive. Before you said I was on the defensive do you think I was on the defensive? I *wasn't* on the defensive.

NAOMI   I'm sorry. O.K.? I'm sorry.

BERNARD *(Coldly)*   That was a castrating remark.

NAOMI *(Amazed)*   Saying I'm *sorry?*

BERNARD *(Nastily)*   *Don't* take it out of context. I'm an authority on castrating remarks. Women *always* try to get away with them on me. They *never* do. I can recognize a castrating remark a hundred miles away!
   (THEY *stare at each other glumly)*

NAOMI *(Softly)*   Can I say something? (HE *nods)* You're not going to believe this but it's true.

BERNARD *(Impatiently)*   Sure. Sure.

NAOMI   I—I didn't mean to make a castrating remark.

BERNARD   Sure. Sure.

NAOMI   Sometimes they just come out.

BERNARD   Yeah.

NAOMI   It's like sometimes every word I say is exactly like my *mother!* I could *kill* myself. *Some* things are a mistake. (SHE *touches him*) Not everything is deliberate. (HE *looks at her with warmth.* THEY *touch hands*) Want to try again?

BERNARD *(Withdraws)* The alcohol—you know— It wouldn't. I couldn't— The alcohol—*(Pauses to collect himself)* How about tomorrow?

NAOMI   If I ask a question will it offend you?

BERNARD   I don't know. Try.

NAOMI   You want to go home now, don't you?

BERNARD   Well, I wouldn't say— Well, we *are* sort of finished here, aren't we?

NAOMI   You're very uncomfortable.

BERNARD *(Weakly)*   Well, I've got a lot on my mind lately. Southeast Asia and everything. *(Pause as* SHE *stares at him unconvinced)* Nuclear holocaust. *(Pause)* The depression.

NAOMI   What depression?

BERNARD   Mine.

NAOMI   It's like you've already left. It's like you're out of the room right now.

BERNARD *(Giggles uncomfortably)*   I guess I am. I often don't know until I'm told.

NAOMI   Listen. This is a difficult question to ask. Do you—do you *enjoy* making love?

BERNARD *(Leaps up)*   Listen! I just had a little too much to drink!

NAOMI   Look, I know it's hard to talk about. Will you please listen to me for a minute. I'm a difficult person, all right?

BERNARD Boy!
(HE *sits down*)

NAOMI But tell me—when it's over—do you feel *happy? (No answer)* Can't you talk to me? Then answer this. Do you feel *good? (No answer)* Listen. Do me a favor? This one favor? You don't have to talk about it, all right? We'll do it so you don't have to talk about it. *I'll* ask the question—and *you* blink once for yes and twice for no. *(HE looks at her as if SHE's mad)* When it's over do you feel happy? *(Long pause)* Once for yes—twice for no. *(Long pause. HE blinks twice. SHE nods knowingly)* Do you feel —guilty? *(HE blinks once instantly)* Everybody I know feels guilty! Why do you feel guilty? *(No answer)* Is it because we don't really know each other? You feel we're not really having a relationship? *(No answer)* Blink.

BERNARD *(Explodes)* I'm *tired* of blinking! Well, *is* there a relationship? Is there? Is there? We meet at a party, we talk maybe twenty minutes in all, we come up here and I can't do it. I admit it—you've broken me down! I don't like being in this position, I *don't* enjoy it—you're right there—I don't—and you're right again—I *do* feel guilty! And I want to thank you. I've gotten more sexual gratification out of this speech I just made than if I *had* gone to bed with you!

NAOMI Don't you understand what the trouble is?

BERNARD I'm that rare kind of person who can't have sex out of context. *I* want a relationship! I'm a *nut!*

NAOMI Crap! *(HE winces)* Why does every bourgeois male I meet have to put a value judgment on sex?

BERNARD *(Frostily)* You don't frighten me. I am not afraid of the term bourgeois!

NAOMI Everybody has to prove it's not *wrong!* Why for Godsakes? Why? You don't mind cheating on your income tax and *that's* wrong, you don't mind lying to girls who you're tired of and *that's* wrong, but the one thing that's super-wrong you can't admit is wrong!

BERNARD There is nothing wrong with the sexual act. Properly administered it can be beautiful. Where are you from? Out of the dark ages?

NAOMI Don't believe it for a minute.

BERNARD Psychologists tell us—

NAOMI Don't believe it.

BERNARD I *do* believe it. It's not wrong!

NAOMI Then it must be *right.*

BERNARD *(Uncertainly)* Well, just because it may not be right doesn't mean it's wrong. Sex *is* clean you know.

NAOMI Don't believe it!

BERNARD It is! Psychologists tell us—

NAOMI They're lying! Nobody really believes sex is clean.

BERNARD Psychologists tell us—

NAOMI Nobody believes it. Do you believe it?

BERNARD Mine is a unique case.

NAOMI They're lying! That's what confuses everybody. You can't turn sex into something pure like brushing your teeth! Sex is exactly what you thought it was when you first learned about it!

BERNARD *(With growing excitement)* You mean on the streets? It's dirty?

NAOMI *(Nods)* Sex is dirty!

BERNARD *(Alarmed)* It *is* dirty! As soon as I said it I *knew!*

NAOMI Right!

BERNARD It is! It is! It always has been! It always will be! They *were* lying to me! It's *dirty!* It's *evil!* It's *bad!*

NAOMI Right!

BERNARD *(Delighted)* I can *enjoy* it now!

NAOMI My own!
> (SHE *opens her arms,* BERNARD *emits an ugly laugh.* THEY *embrace violently)*

Blackout

OH,
GOD.

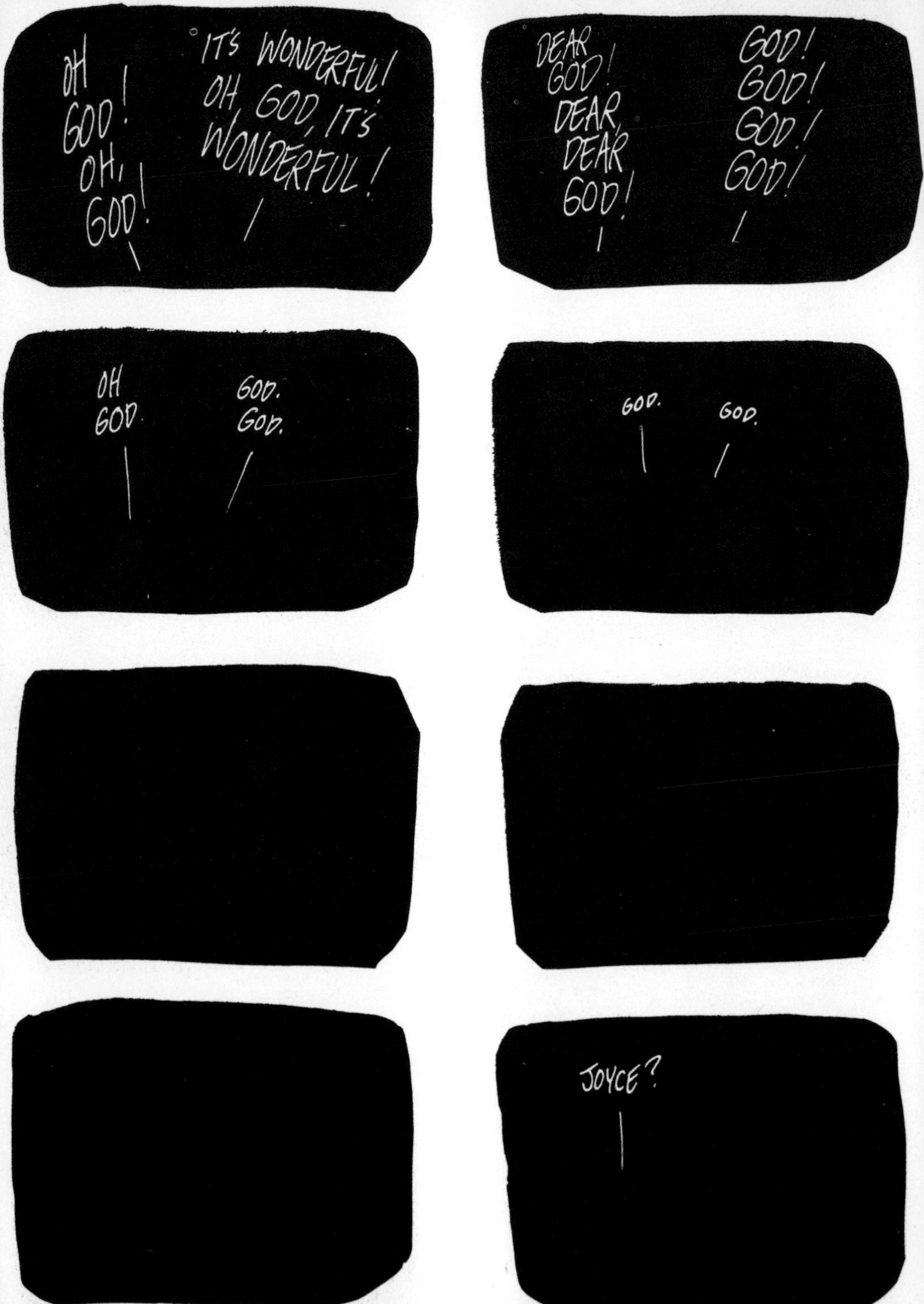
OH GOD! OH, GOD!
IT'S WONDERFUL! OH GOD, IT'S WONDERFUL!
DEAR GOD! DEAR, DEAR GOD!
GOD! GOD! GOD! GOD!
OH GOD.
GOD. GOD.
GOD.
GOD.
JOYCE?

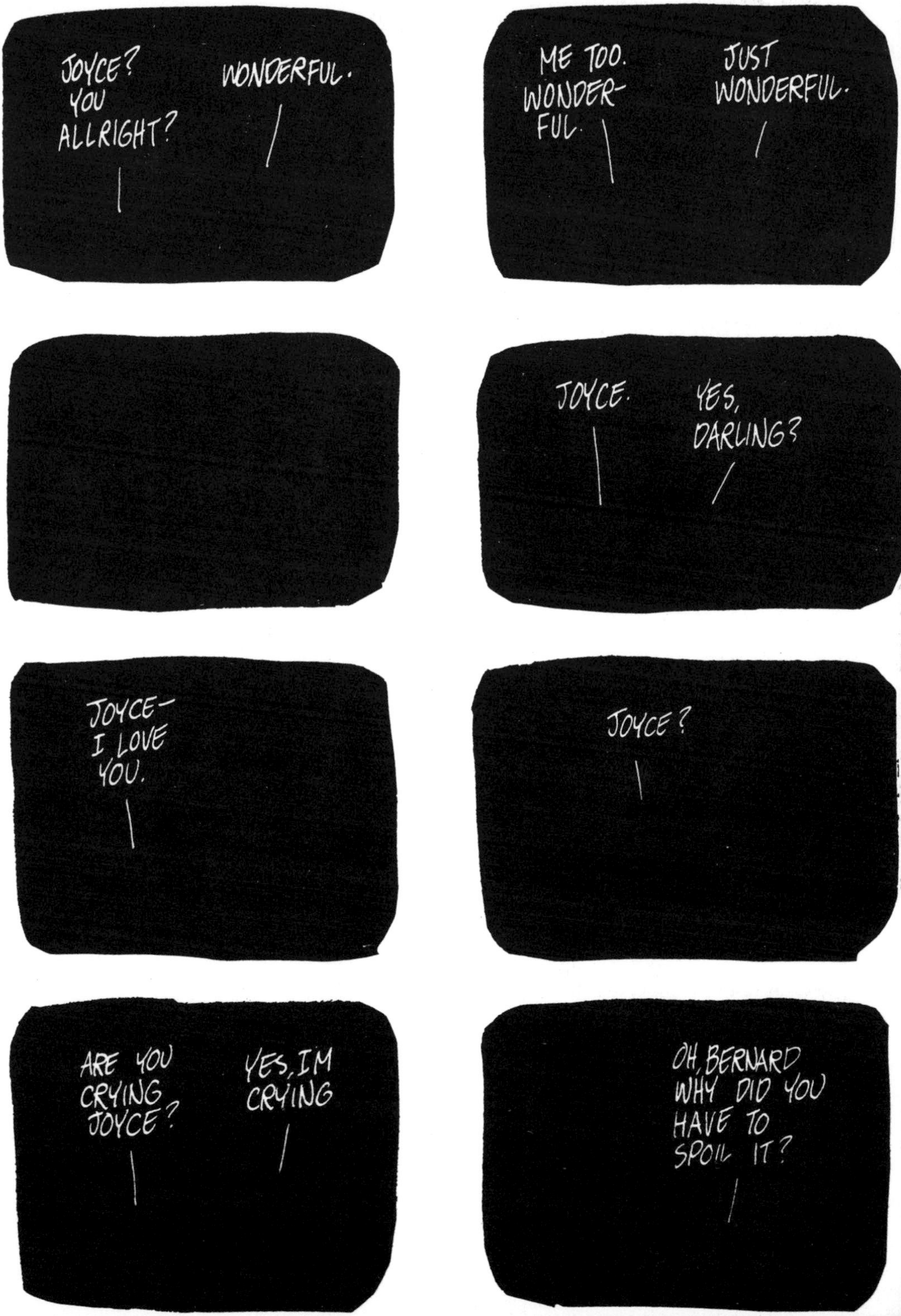
JOYCE? YOU ALLRIGHT?
WONDERFUL.
ME TOO. WONDERFUL.
JUST WONDERFUL.
JOYCE.
YES, DARLING?
JOYCE- I LOVE YOU.
JOYCE?
ARE YOU CRYING JOYCE?
YES, IM CRYING
OH, BERNARD WHY DID YOU HAVE TO SPOIL IT?

AND WHAT DID I SAY NEXT?

YOU TOLD ME YOU LOVED ME AND WERE SORRY FOR THE WAY YOU TREATED ME. DON'T YOU REMEMBER?

OH, SURE. SURE. THAT'S WHEN I TOOK YOU HOME, RIGHT?

NO. YOU WANTED TO GO ON A FERRY RIDE, DON'T YOU REMEMBER? YOU APOLOGIZED TO ME ALL THE WAY- BOTH WAYS.

OH, THAT'S RIGHT, SURE. **THEN** I TOOK YOU HOME.

NO. DON'T YOU REMEMBER? WE COULDN'T FIND A TAXI AND YOU SAID IT WAS YOUR FAULT BE- CAUSE YOU WERE SUCH A ROTTEN GUY AND YOU BE- GAN TO CRY.

I'M NOT SURE I REMEM- BER THAT.

AND I SAID YOU WERE A LONELY GUY AND YOU JUST HAD A LITTLE TOO MUCH TO DRINK AND WHY NOT, EVERYBODY HAS A RIGHT ON NEW YEAR'S EVE.

THAT'S A VERY UNDER- STANDING THING TO SAY.

THEN YOU ASKED ME TO MARRY YOU.

REMEMBER?

REMEMBER?

BERNARD, DO
YOU OR DON'T
YOU REMEMBER?

SLAM.

WHAT A TERRIFYING
WAY TO START
A YEAR.

I ALWAYS USED TO NOTICE GIRLS ON THE BUS IF THEY WERE WRITING IN A NOTEBOOK.

I'D FIGURE THEY WERE **WRITERS** AND I'D WANT TO GO OVER AND START A CONVERSATION ABOUT HOW **I** USED TO WRITE A LOT IN SCHOOL—

AND I WAS GOING TO DO IT **AGAIN** SOMEDAY. AND THEY'D BE ABLE TO TELL FROM THE WAY I TALKED AND MY PERSONAL CHARM AND EVERYTHING THAT IF I EVER **WANTED** TO I **COULD** BE A VERY GOOD WRITER.

AND JUST TO SHOW THEM THAT I WASN'T A LOT OF HOT AIR I'D SAY **NAMES** TO THEM - LIKE "**BELLOW**" AND "**MALAMUD**" AND "**ALBEE**"—YOU KNOW, SO THEY'D BEGIN TO **TRUST** ME AND LET ME LOOK AT WHAT THEY HAD WRITTEN.

AND IT WOULD BE **GREAT!** REALLY **GREAT!** NOT QUITE AS GREAT AS WHAT **I** COULD WRITE IF I EVER GOT AROUND TO IT. LESS GREAT, BUT GREAT NEVERTHELESS.

AND I'D MAKE A
FEW CRITICISMS-
YOU KNOW, ABOUT
**SENTENCE STRUC-
TURE** - THINGS
THAT WOULD
SHOW I KNEW
WHAT I WAS
TALKING ABOUT.

AND WHEN THEY'D GET
OFF THE BUS THEY'D
BE SURPRISED
BECAUSE INSTEAD OF
GETTING OFF WITH
THEM I'D SAY:
"GOODBYE."

AND THEN THEY'D KNOW
THAT I WASN'T JUST
A **PHONEY** TRYING FOR
A PICKUP AND THEY'D
BE VERY IMPRESSED
WITH ME.

AND **THAT'S**
ALL I'D
WANT.

I JUST
WANT
SOMEBODY
TO BE
IMPRESSED
WITH ME.

ONE NIGHT- AT A PARTY- I WAS IN AN ARGUMENT WHEN SUDDENLY, JUST WHEN I WAS ABOUT TO APPLY THE CRUSHER AND QUOTE STATISTICS FROM THE WALL STREET JOURNAL - I REALIZED I DIDN'T BELIEVE A **SINGLE WORD I** WAS SAYING.

AND I DIDN'T BELIEVE A SINGLE WORD MY OPPONENT WAS SAYING. AND I THOUGHT FURTHER AND I REALIZED THAT I DIDN'T BELIEVE A SINGLE ARGUMENT I HAD HEARD ALL EVENING OR A SINGLE NEWSPAPER EDITORIAL I HAD READ IN **MONTHS.**

AND THEN IT CAME TO ME THAT I HADN'T BELIEVED ANYTHING ANYBODY HAD TOLD ME IN **YEARS.** THAT DEEP INSIDE THE ONLY THING I **REALLY** BELIEVED WAS THAT **EVERYBODY** WAS **LYING!**

THAT IT WAS **ALL** SPECIAL PLEADING.. GIRLS! JOBS! GOVERNMENTS! ME! **EVERYTHING!**

AND SO I GOT
VERY DEPRESSED.
BECAUSE IF LIES
WERE THE ONLY
THING ANYONE
COULD BELIEVE
IN HOW DOES
ONE GO ABOUT
SELECTING THE
BEST LIE. THE
ONE THAT MAKES
YOU **FEEL** BETTER?

BUT THEN **ANOTHER** THOUGHT CAME TO
MIND- WAS **I** SO WELL INFORMED
THAT I COULD AFFORD TO MAKE
SUCH STATEMENTS? WEREN'T
THERE OTHERS IN POSITIONS OF
AUTHORITY FAR BETTER TRAINED
IN THE COMPLEXITY OF OUR TIMES
WHOSE GUIDANCE I SHOULD ACCEPT-
ESPECIALLY WHEN MY **OWN**
CONCLUSIONS WERE SO BADLY
CONFUSED?

AND WASN'T MY BELIEF
THAT EVERYTHING WAS A
LIE ONLY A DEVICE TO
ESCAPE RESPONSIBILITY?
REALIZING THIS I
BECAME **HUMBLE**. I
CAME TO A **NEW**
BELIEF...

-TO ACCEPT
GUIDANCE.
TO HAVE
TRUST IN
THE GOOD
SENSE OF
THE EXPERTS.

THAT IS
WHAT I
HAVE
FINALLY
COME
TO
BELIEVE.

MY LIE,
RIGHT
OR
WRONG.

LIFE
IS A
GAME.

NO. LIFE IS
THE WEARING
OF MASKS.
EVERYBODY
KNOWS THAT.

FOR EXAMPLE, UP TILL
A MINUTE AGO WE
WERE PLAYING THE
LOVE GAME. NOW
WERE PLAYING THE
ARGUMENT GAME.

THAT'S ALL A MASK.
THE **ARGUMENT**
MASK IS A COVER-
UP FOR OUR DIS-
APPOINTMENT IN
THE **LOVE** MASK.

IF YOU DIDN'T HAVE
THE TOO-COOL ATTI-
TUDE THAT LOVE IS
A **MASK** I MIGHT
NOT HAVE BEEN
DISAPPOINTED IN
THE LOVE GAME.

AND IF YOU THINK
THAT BEING
TREATED LIKE A
TEAM PLAYER
IS MY IDEA OF A
GOOD MASK
YOU'RE OUT OF
YOUR MIND.

I NEVER HAD A
BEST FRIEND
WHEN I WAS
A KID-

WHEN EVERYBODY **ELSE**
ON THE BLOCK HAD A
BEST FRIEND **WE**
MOVED IN. ALL
THE BEST FRIENDS
WERE ALREADY
TAKEN!

HAVING A BEST FRIEND IS
A VERY IMPORTANT
PERIOD IN A PERSON'S
MATURATION AND **I**
HAPPEN TO HAVE A
BEST FRIEND GAP!
THAT'S WHY I NEVER
REALLY **MATURED!**

SUDDENLY I WAS TOO **OLD**
TO HAVE ONE. SO AS A
SUBSTITUTE I MADE
BEST FRIENDS OUT OF
THE **GIRLS** I WENT
WITH. **THEY** CONFIDED
EVERYTHING IN ME. **I**
CONFIDED EVERYTHING
IN **THEM.**

THEN THE FIRST TIME I'D **TOUCH** THEM THEY'D **BREAK OFF!** "I THOUGHT YOU WERE MY **BEST FRIEND**," THEY'D SAY.

SO IT'S TOO LATE TO BE BEST FRIENDS WITH MEN. AND IT'S TOO FRUSTRATING TO BE BEST FRIENDS WITH GIRLS.

SO WHILE OTHER GUYS ARE BUSY DREAMING OF THE IDEAL **GIRL** OR THE IDEAL **CAREER-** I DREAM OF THE IDEAL **BEST FRIEND.**

THE MARK OF A MEDIOCRE MAN IS A MEDIOCRE IDEAL.

I DON'T UNDER-
STAND HOW IT
HAPPENED BUT
WHEN I WOKE
UP YESTERDAY
MORNING—
I **KNEW**—
SOMETHING
HAD CHANGED!

I DIDN'T
LOOK LIKE
ME ANY-
MORE!

I LOOKED
LIKE
CARY
GRANT.

I LOOKED
IN THE
MIRROR
AND SURE
ENOUGH—
THERE IT
WAS—CARY
GRANT.

I WALKED
DOWN THE
STREET AND
I COULD
SEE IT IN
THE WAY
PEOPLE
STARED
AT ME—
CARY
GRANT.

I WENT TO THE OF-
FICE AND EVERYBODY
SEEMED **SHY** IN MY
PRESENCE. GIRLS
STARTED HANGING
AROUND MY DESK.
MY DESK. THE
BOSS OFFERED ME
A JOB IN THE
PARIS OFFICE.
CARY GRANT.

I CALLED UP THE MOST BEAUTIFUL GIRL I KNEW. SHE SAID SHE HAD A DATE BUT SHE'D BREAK IT. SHE SAID SHE'D PICK UP TICKETS TO THE THEATER. CARY GRANT.

WE WENT DANCING AFTER THE THEATER. I DIDN'T EVEN KNOW I KNEW **HOW!** PEOPLE FORMED A CIRCLE AROUND US AND APPLAUDED.

I WENT HOME FLOATING. I WENT TO SLEEP DREAMING. THIS MORNING I WOKE UP AND KNEW SOMETHING HAD CHANGED.

BACK TO BERNARD MERGEN-DEILER.

FOR PLAIN PEOPLE THERE IS NO SUCH THING AS A PERMANENT CARY GRANT.

HOW DO YOU DO,
MR. MERGEN-
DEILER. I'M
YOUR
GROWN-UP.

YOU'RE MY
WHAT?

SURELY YOU'VE ALWAYS
WANTED A GROWN-UP?
SOMEBODY WHO TAKES
OVER THOSE PETTY DAY-
TO-DAY AFFAIRS WHICH
SO COMPLICATE ONE'S
LIFE AND WHO HANDLES
THEM CLEANLY AND
EFFICIENTLY.

SOMEBODY WHO WILL NOT ALLOW
YOUR INSURANCE TO LAPSE, YOUR
RENT TO FALL OVERDUE, YOUR
CAR TO BREAK DOWN. SOMEBODY
WHO WILL NOT BE NERVOUS IN
REGARD TO CALLING THE LAND-
LORD ABOUT REPAIRS, THE
GIRL FRIEND ABOUT BREAKING
A DATE, THE BOSS ABOUT A
NEEDED RAISE.

IN OTHER WORDS SOMEBODY WHO
IS TRAINED TO DO ALL THOSE
ADULT THINGS TOO MANY OF US
HAVE BEEN ASKED TO DO SINCE
CHILDHOOD AND STILL CAN'T QUITE
MANAGE. SOMEBODY WHO IS
WILLING AND HAPPY TO STAND
ON YOUR OWN TWO FEET FOR
YOU, TO FIGHT ALL YOUR
BATTLES, TO MAKE ALL YOUR
DIFFICULT DECISIONS — I.e., YOUR
GROWN-UP!

YOU MEAN I WON'T EVER HAVE TO MAKE A DECISION AGAIN?

ONCE IN YOUR
EMPLOY I,
YOUR GROWN-UP,
WILL MAKE
THEM ALL!

IT'S UNBELIEVABLE! IT'S WHAT I'VE DREAMED OF ALL MY LIFE! WHAT DO YOU WANT ME TO PAY YOU?

GEE, I DON'T KNOW. WHAT DO YOU THINK I'M WORTH?

YOU DISGUST ME!

CAN'T YOU KEEP YOUR HANDS TO YOURSELF FOR ONE MINUTE?

I DON'T KNOW WHY YOU THINK YOU BROUGHT ME HERE BUT I CAME TO SEE A MOVIE!

IF THATS WHAT A DATE WITH YOU IS GOING TO BE LIKE WE MAY AS WELL PUT A STOP TO IT RIGHT NOW!

YOU POOR DEAR. I FRIGHTENED
YOU HALF TO DEATH, DIDN'T I?

WHEN I OPEN
MY EYES
THERE WILL
BE WORLD
PEACE.

YOU
ONLY
WISH.

AND A TELEPHONE
CALL FROM MY
MOTHER SAYING,
"YOU WERE RIGHT,
I WAS WRONG!"

WHAT
DO YOU
WANT?
NOTHING
CHANGES.

AND A GOOD JOB.
AND A SENSE OF
PURPOSE. AND
MUSCLES.

GIVE IN.
WHAT
DOES IT
GET
YOU?

AND A BEAUTIFUL GIRL FROM
A NICE BACKGROUND WHO'LL
SAY, "I'VE FOUND YOU, MY
DARLING, FOUND YOU
AT LAST!"

DON'T EXPECT
TOO MUCH
AND YOU
WON'T BE
DISAPPOINTED.

ALL WHEN
I OPEN
MY EYES.

DREAMER.

I'VE FOUND YOU,
MY DARLING, _
FOUND YOU
AT LAST!

WHEN I OPEN
MY EYES
HE'LL BE
BACK.

HELLO, MR. MERGENDEILER? THIS IS MISS 711 OF THE TELEPHONE COMPANY, FORMERLY MISS BUTTERFIELD.

WHAT I'M CALLING ABOUT, MR. MERGENDEILER, IS YOUR REFUSAL BY REGISTERED LETTER TO ALLOW US TO CHANGE YOUR PRESENT EXCHANGE FROM **CANAL 6** TO **3441515.**

YES, WE ARE ALL AWARE OF THE ALLEGED CHARGES OF DEHUMAN-IZATION, MR. MERGENDEILER. **WE** TOO READ THE NEWS-PAPER EDITORIALS. HOW **ELSE** WOULD WE KNOW FROM WHICH PAPERS TO WITHDRAW OUR ADVERTISING?

BUT, SIR, AREN'T YOU OVERLOOKING PROGRESS? THROUGH OUR NEW SYSTEM OF DIGITAL COM-PUTER REFLEX DIALING YOUR CALLS WILL GO THROUGH MUCH FASTER AND AT A CONSIDERABLE SAVING WHICH WE CAN **THEN** PASS ON TO **YOU** IN THE FORM OF **FURTHER** DEHUMANIZATION.

FOR EXAMPLE, TO FACILITATE A MORE EFFICIENT INFORMATION SERVICE ALL **FUTURE** TELEPHONE BOOKS WILL DELETE **NAMES.** INSTEAD, EACH SUBSCRIBER WILL HAVE HIS **OWN** CODE NUMBER. OF COURSE, **UNLISTED** CODE NUMBERS WILL COST A LITTLE EXTRA.

HENCEFORTH MR. MERGENDEILER, **YOU** WILL BE MR. **316.** EXCEPT FOR OUT OF STATE CALLS WHEN YOU WILL BE MR. 555316! I **ASSURE** YOU, MR. 316, IT'S ALL PERFECTLY SIMPLE ONCE YOU GET USED TO — HELLO? **HELLO?**

OH, SOMETIMES — SOMETIMES THESE RECALCITRANT SUBSCRIBERS MAKE ME WANT TO CRY.

DON'T CRY, 711.

WHY, 477 — YOU BROUGHT ME A 9.

I FEEL
RESPONSIBLE
FOR
EVERYTHING.

FOR INSTANCE,
IF THE WORLD
BLEW UP
TOMORROW
AND **I**
WAS THE
ONLY
SURVIVOR—
YOU KNOW
HOW I'D
FEEL?

VERY
DEFENSIVE.

AS IF IT
WERE MY
IDEA IN THE
FIRST PLACE.
BUT THEN
I TELL
MYSELF
THAT'S
CRAZY!

I DIDN'T
BLOW UP
THE WORLD.
I JUST
THOUGHT
ABOUT
BLOWING UP
THE WORLD.
IS **THINKING**
A CRIME?

BUT NO
MATTER
HOW I
ARGUE
I KNOW
ITS ONLY
AN **ALIBI.**

THAT'S
WHY I
SMILE A
LOT AT
PEOPLE.

I DON'T
ASK
THAT
THEY
LIKE ME—

ALL I
ASK IS
THEY FIND
ME **NOT**
GUILTY.

BOOM.

YES, THIS IS DIANNE. OH, HELLO, HUEY— WELL, WHY **SHOULDN'T** I SOUND ANGRY? YOU WERE SUPPOSED TO CALL ME LAST WEEK. WHY SHOULD **I** CALL YOU IF YOU DON'T CALL ME? NO, I'M NOT **LIKE** THAT! THE BOY CALLS **ME**!

NO, I CAN'T RIGHT NOW. BECAUSE I HAVE A DINNER DATE. NO, I **WON'T** BREAK IT. NO, BECAUSE IT'S CRUEL. CERTAINLY I WANT TO SEE YOU. BUT IF I BROKE A DATE WITH **THIS** BOY HOW WOULD YOU KNOW I WOULDN'T BREAK A DATE WITH **YOU**?

NOW, YOU STOP TALKING THAT WAY. YOU KNOW HOW IT EMBARRASSES ME. WELL, I'LL **THINK** ABOUT IT. MAYBE I'LL CALL YOU BACK IN FIVE MINUTES. I SAID **MAYBE**. ALL RIGHT FIVE MINUTES.

HELLO, BERNARD?

I'M GLAD I CAUGHT YOU, DEAR. LISTEN, I HATE TO DO THIS BUT I HAD A SIMPLY **MISERABLE** DAY AT THE OFFICE AND I WONDERED IF WE COULDN'T POSTPONE THINGS TONIGHT.

I KNEW YOU'D UNDERSTAND, DEAR. I'D BE **ROTTEN** COMPANY. YOU'RE AN ANGEL. CALL ME NEXT WEEK.

HELLO, HUEY?

WELL, CAN I SPEAK TO HUEY, PLEASE? HE **CAN'T** HAVE GONE OUT. WHAT DO YOU MEAN HE'S GONE OUT? SAY, WHAT ARE YOU DOING IN HIS PLACE **ANYWAY**? HELLO! **HELLO!**

HELLO, BERNARD?

LISTEN, DEAR—I CAN'T STAND MYSELF FOR TREATING YOU THIS WAY. YOU'RE AN ANGEL, BUT IT'S **NOT** ALL RIGHT. NO, I'LL PULL MYSELF TOGETHER **SOMEHOW**. SAME TIME, SAME RESTAURANT, THEN? I'M **DYING** TO SEE YOU!

IS **HE** GOING TO PAY.

YOUR FATHER CALLED AT 3:00 AND
WANTED TO KNOW WHY YOU HADN'T
CALLED YOUR MOTHER. BUT DON'T
TELL HER HE TOLD YOU TO. FAITH
CALLED AT 3:05 AND SAID IF YOU
DON'T CALL HER BY
5:00 SHE WILL KILL
HERSELF. LOLA
CALLED AT
3:30. NO
MESSAGE.

YOUR FATHER CALLED AT 4:00 AND SAID
IF YOU DIDN'T CALL YOUR MOTHER HE
WOULD KILL HIMSELF. LOLA CALLED
AT 4:30 AND SAID IF SHE DIDN'T
HEAR FROM YOU BY 7:00 SHE
WOULD KILL HER-
SELF. FAITH CALLED
AT 5:05 AND LEFT
WORD THAT SHE
WAS GOING TO
KILL HERSELF.

ANYTHING
ELSE?

ONLY ONE
THING
MORE,
SIR.

OH, HUEY! I LOVE
YOU! I LOVE YOU!
I LOVE YOU!

WE USED TO BUDDY AROUND A LOT, JULES AND ME - CLOSE FRIENDS - YOU KNOW WHAT I MEAN? CONFIDANTS.

AND THEN HE BRINGS THIS **GIRL** AROUND - OH SURE, NICE ENOUGH AND EVERYTHING. AND HE SAYS TO ME - "BERNARD, I'M GETTING MARRIED." HE NEVER SAID A **WORD** ABOUT HER **BEFORE**. WELL, WHAT WAS HE TRYING TO **PROVE**?

THEN WE GOT INTO A HASSLE ABOUT THE CEREMONY - JULES WANTED IT ONE WAY, **THIS** GIRL WANTED IT ANOTHER WAY, AND **I** WANTED IT THE WAY JULES SAID BECAUSE IT MADE THE MOST SENSE.

SO AFTER THAT THIS GIRL GOT VERY TENSE WITH ME. NOT EXACTLY UNFRIENDLY BUT **AGGRESSIVELY** TENSE. LIKE WHEN WE DROVE TO THE CEREMONY YOU SHOULD **SEE** THE WAY SHE JAMMED HER WAY INTO OUR CAR, EVEN THOUGH THERE WAS HARDLY EVEN ROOM ENOUGH FOR **ME**.

AND AFTER THEY DID **IT** I WAS, OF COURSE, HAPPY FOR HIM, BUT NOW I DIDN'T HAVE ANYBODY TO **TALK** TO. I STARTED GOING OUT WITH GIRLS **EVERY** NIGHT INSTEAD OF JUST ON WEEK-ENDS.

NOW OURS IS HARDLY EVEN A FRIENDSHIP ANYMORE. HE SEEMS TO TALK TO THIS GIRL MORE THAN HE TALKS TO ME. "JULES," I SAID, "**WHO** KNOWS YOU LONGER? WHY TAKE A CHANCE ON GETTING IRRESPONSIBLE ADVICE?"

BUT- I DON'T KNOW- SOMEHOW WE STOPPED BEING CLOSE. I CALL HIM MORE THAN HE CALLS ME. AND THERE ARE A LOT OF **PAUSES.** HE'S **CHANGED.**

NEW GIRLS **ALWAYS** COME ALONG, BUT AT MY AGE WHERE AM I GOING TO FIND ANOTHER BUDDY?

I'VE ALWAYS LOVED TO DO **IMITATIONS**. BUT I COULD NEVER GET ANYONE TO **LISTEN**.

BECAUSE AT THE PARTIES I WENT TO EVERYONE **ELSE** DID **FEATURE** IMITATIONS—HUMPHREY BOGART, JIMMY CAGNEY, CARY GRANT—AND ALL **I** KNEW HOW TO DO WERE **B** IMITATIONS—LIONEL ATWILL, GEORGE ZUCCO, WALLACE FORD.

PEOPLE WOULD WALK OUT ON MY IMITATIONS. ID DO A **GREAT** GEORGE ZUCCO, BUT NOBODY WOULD CARE. ID DO A **CLASSIC** LIONEL ATWILL, BUT EVERYONE WOULD GO FOR A DRINK!

TILL ONE NIGHT I JUST COULDN'T STAND IT ANYMORE. MY LIONEL ATWILL GOT DRUNKER AND DRUNKER, MY GEORGE ZUCCO GOT MORE AND MORE MUMBLY, MY WALLACE FORD WAS PRACTICALLY INCOHERENT.

THEN, JUST WHEN EVERYONE WAS ABOUT TO GO HOME I RIPPED OPEN MY SHIRT AND BEGAN TO SHOUT! I BEGAN TO TELL EVERYONE OFF—THE **PARTY**—THE **PEOPLE**—THE WHOLE **WORLD**—PUSHING ME AROUND, NEVER GIVING ME A CHANCE!

BUT IT WASN'T **MY** VOICE THAT WAS TELLING THEM OFF. IN THE MIDDLE OF A SENTENCE I REALIZED IT WAS **JOHN GARFIELD'S**. AND I NEVER EVEN KNEW I COULD **DO** JOHN GARFIELD!

I DID JOHN GARFIELD IN **"FOUR DAUGHTERS"**, IN **"DUST BE MY DESTINY,"** IN **"BODY AND SOUL"**. THE ROOM DIDN'T MOVE FOR HOURS. THE WOMEN BEGAN TO CRY.

NOW'DAYS WHEN I COME INTO A PARTY THE PIANO PLAYER QUIETS, THE FOLK SINGERS LEAVE, THE **OTHER** IMITATORS SIT AT MY FEET. I OPEN MY SHIRT, STICK A CIGARET IN THE CORNER OF MY MOUTH - AND I DO JOHN GARFIELD.

I'M A **STAR**.

SHE REMINDED ME OF DORIS.

HE'S SOME KIND OF MANIAC.

EVERY GIRL REMINDS ME OF DORIS.

HE'S GOING TO FOLLOW ME HOME AND KILL ME IN MY SLEEP.

WHO'M I KIDDING? THERE IS NO DORIS. A **DREAM** DORIS— THAT'S WHO I'M PINING FOR!

DOES HE KNOW I'VE GOT A POLICE LOCK AND FOUR CHAINS ON THE DOOR?

THE **REAL** DORIS IS A DES-**TROYER**! A KILLER! WELL, WHY NOT? THEY'RE **ALL** KILLERS!

I'VE GOT BARS ON THE WINDOWS AND A POLICE WHISTLE BY MY BED. HOW DOES HE EXPECT TO GET AWAY WITH IT?

WHY DO I LET THEM DO IT TO ME? EVERY TIME ITS THE SAME. THERES NO-ONE YOU CAN TRUST.

NEVER MIND. HE'LL GET IN. MEN **ALWAYS** HAVE THEIR WAY. IF HE WANTS TO KILL ME I'LL JUST HAVE TO LET HIM HAVE HIS WAY AND KILL ME.

THAT GIRL BACK THERE. COULD SHE HAVE BEEN THE **ONE**? COULD SHE HAVE BEEN **DIFFERENT**?

ALL MY LIFE MEN HAVE KILLED ME, ALL EX-CEPT GEORGIE. WHY DID I SEND GEORGIE AWAY?

WHY DON'T I STOP TORTURING MYSELF? NO ONE'S DIFFERENT! SHE'S A KILLER TOO!

I'M GOING HOME AND CALL THE POLICE.

FOR A NICE GUY WHY AM I SUCH A VICTIM.

THE POLICE WILL COME OVER AND KILL ME.

OUTSIDE I SEEM TO BE STABLE AND STEADY— BUT ITS ONLY A **DISGUISE**.  INSIDE I SEE MY-SELF AS SELF PITYING, INDECISIVE, LONELY AND INEFFECTUAL.

AND FROM TIME TO TIME I'D GO OUT WITH BRIGHT GIRLS WHO HAD IN-SIGHT AND THEY'D SAY—  "I CAN SEE RIGHT THROUGH YOU, BERNARD MERGENDEILER."

"WHILE OUTSIDE YOU SEEM TO BE STABLE AND STEADY— **INSIDE** YOU'RE REALLY SELF PITYING, IN-DECISIVE, LONELY AND INEFFECTUAL."  SO OF COURSE I'D FALL IN LOVE WITH THEM.

BUT THEN **LAST** WEEK I WENT OUT WITH AN EXTREMELY BRIGHT GIRL— RADCLIFFE GRADUATE— WORKS FOR TIME INC.— AND **SHE** SAID— " I CAN SEE RIGHT THROUGH YOU BERNARD MERGENDEILER."

"WHILE OUTSIDE YOU SEEM TO BE STABLE AND STEADY — **INSIDE** YOU'RE CRUEL, BRUTISH, SINISTER AND SELFISH!"

CAN YOU **IMAGINE**?

I ARGUED WITH HER ALL EVENING! I **TOLD** HER THAT ALL THE **OTHER** GIRLS WHO THOUGHT THEY SAW THROUGH ME —

— DIDN'T SEE WHAT **SHE** THOUGHT SHE SAW THROUGH ME!

BUT WHILE WE ARGUED I BEGAN LETTING OUT AN UNCONTROLLABLE **LOW, UGLY** LAUGH —

AND THEN, EVERY ONCE IN A WHILE, I FOUND MYSELF **TWISTING** HER ARM!

FINALLY SHE WENT HOME. SHE SAID IT WAS THE MOST MISERABLE DATE SHE'D EVER HAD IN HER LIFE.

I FELT ABSOLUTELY **MARVELOUS!**

I MEET A GIRL AND I BUY HER THINGS AND SHE REJECTS ME AND **WHAT** DO I SAY?

I SAY— "THIS WAS AN UNHEALTHY RELATIONSHIP BUT I HAVE LEARNED FROM IT."

SO I MEET **ANOTHER** GIRL AND SHE'S DIFFERENT AND I BUY HER THINGS AND SHE REJECTS ME AND **WHAT** DO I SAY?

I SAY— "THIS WAS AN UNHEALTHY RELATIONSHIP BUT IT HAS **MATURED** ME."

THEN I MEET A NEW GIRL WHO'S THE BEST YET AND I BUY HER THINGS AND SHE REJECTS ME AND WHAT, OH WHAT DO I SAY?

I SAY— "THIS WAS AN UNHEALTHY RELATIONSHIP BUT IT HAS GIVEN ME INSIGHT."

TIME AFTER TIME FOLLOWING EACH REJECTION I TELL MYSELF I'M **WISER** IN KNOWLEGE, I'M **WISER** IN EXPERIENCE, I'M **WISER** IN DEPTH.

I'VE COME TO LOOK ON MYSELF AS THE RENAISSANCE MAN OF THE REJECTEES.

HELLO, DOGGIE!

HA HA, BARON—
DON'T BOTHER THE
LITTLE GIRL.

NICE
DOGGIE,
NICE—

COME ON, BARON—
HERE, OLD FELLA—

NICE
DOGGIE—
GOOD
DOGGIE—

HERE, BARON! HERE, I SAY!
YOU, SIR! HERE, BARON! THIS
IS BERNARD SPEAKING!
HERE, YOU BARON!

FOR A LONG WHILE IT WAS ALWAYS EDDIE, MILTON AND ME MAKING THE ROUNDS. AT PARTIES IT WAS ALWAYS EDDIE, MILTON AND ME.

AND AS OUR OTHER FRIENDS - LENNIE, JERRY AND CHARLIE ALL GOT MARRIED AND HAD KIDS IT WAS STILL EDDIE, MILTON AND ME.

LENNIE, JERRY AND CHARLIE HAD US OVER TO DINNER. THEY FIXED US UP WITH GIRLS. THEY KEPT TELLING US WHAT WE WERE MISSING— BUT SOMEHOW WE STAYED SINGLE— EDDIE, MILTON AND ME.

AND WE SAID WE'D **ALWAYS** STAY SINGLE. BUT **PRIVATELY** EACH ONE OF US WAS THINKING— "I DON'T WANT TO BE THE **LAST** TO GO!"

EDDIE WAS THE FIRST TO GO. MILTON AND I WOULD HAVE DINNER AT HIS NEW HOUSE AND LISTEN TO HIM TELL US WHAT WE WERE MISSING.

MILTON WAS THE NEXT TO GO. I'D GO HAVE DINNER AT HIS NEW HOUSE AND LISTEN TO **HIM** TELL ME WHAT I WAS MISSING.

I THOUGHT THERE WAS NOTHING LEFT BUT FOR **ME** TO GET MARRIED. BUT THEN LENNIE GOT DIVORCED. AND THEN JERRY GOT DIVORCED. AND THEN CHARLIE —

SO NOW IT'S ALWAYS THE FOUR OF US MAKING THE ROUNDS AT PARTIES — LENNIE, JERRY, CHARLIE AND ME. BUT IT'S JUST TEMPORARY.

I'M WAITING FOR EDDIE AND MILTON TO COME BACK.

SO HOW
DOES IT
FEEL?

OH, FINE.
FINE. FINE.

YOU
LIKE
IT?

OH, SURE. I MEAN
YOU CAN'T TELL
AN AWFUL LOT
IN THE BEGINNING.

BUT YOU THINK
FROM ALL
INDICATIONS
IT WAS THE
RIGHT MOVE?

WELL, SHE WAS
THE NICEST
GIRL I'D MET
FOR AWHILE.

AND SHE'S
HAPPY? SHE
SEEMS TO
BE HAPPY?

WELL,
NEITHER
ONE OF US
IS A BIG
TALKER.

IF EVER I
THINK I'M
FINALLY
MATURE—

I'LL GIVE MY-
SELF THE
ACID TEST—

I'LL GO
VISIT MY
PARENTS.

AND MY
MOTHER
WILL TELL
ME I'VE
LOST
WEIGHT
AND
DON'T
LOOK
HAPPY.

AND MY FATHER
WILL TELL ME
I SHOULDN'T
BE SUCH A
SMART GUY
AND WHY DON'T
I GIVE MORE
MONEY HOME?

 AND MY MOTHER WILL ASK ME WHY I'M NOT EATING AND ISN'T HER COOKING GOOD ENOUGH FOR ME?

 AND MY FATHER WILL TELL ME A STORY IVE HEARD 500 TIMES BEFORE AND ASK IF HE'S **BORING** ME.

 AND BOTH OF THEM WILL ASK WHY THEY DON'T SEE ME MORE OFTEN.

 AND IF I CAN GET THROUGH THAT WHOLE EVENING WITHOUT FEELING AS IF I'M TEN YEARS OLD—

 I'M A **MAN!**

"AND NOW, THE FINAL CHAPTER IN TONIGHT'S SHOW."

"LADIES AND GENTLE MEN!"

"I'VE JUST LEARNED WE HAVE SOME-ONE VERY SPECIAL IN OUR AUDI-ENCE — MR. BERNARD MERG-ENDEILER! PERHAPS WE CAN COAX HIM UP HERE TO FAVOR US WITH ONE OF HIS IMMORTAL SONGS AND TAP DANCES!"

"WELL, GEE—" YAY! PHWEET! BERNARD!

"LET'S GET HIM UP HERE, BOYS, PLAY HIS THEME!"

"OH, I'M PUTTING ON MY HOMBURG PUTTING ON MY REP TIE, PUTTING ON MY—" YAY! HERE HE COMES!

PHWEET!

"WELL GOSH-GEE-GOSH—"

"AND AS A BONUS SURPRISE - SIT-TING OUT FRONT UNBEKNOWNST TO BERNARD IS HIS FORMER DANCING PARTNER, MISS GINGER MURCH!" GINGER! GINGER! PHWEET!

"GINGER!" "BERNARD!"

WHEN I WAS LITTLE, I LIS-
TENED TO RADIO SERIALS,
READ COMIC BOOKS AND
WENT TO 'B' MOVIES. —

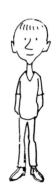

WHEN I GOT A LITTLE OLDER
I LISTENED TO BIG BAND
SWING, READ SLICK MAGA-
ZINES AND WENT TO 'A'   —
MOVIES.

WHEN I GOT EVEN OLDER
I LISTENED TO F·M STEREO,
READ LITERARY QUARTER-
LIES AND WENT TO FOREIGN   —
MOVIES.

AND THEN THE POP-
CULTURE MOVEMENT
BEGAN.

NOW I LISTEN TO OLD
RADIO SERIALS, READ
COMIC BOOKS, AND GO
TO REVIVALS OF 'B' MOVIES.

IN A SOCIETY WITHOUT
STANDARDS WHO NEEDS
TO GROW UP?

I'VE BEEN LYING HERE
A LONG TIME TRYING
TO FIGURE OUT THE
RIGHT **ANSWERS**.

BUT I COULDN'T
COME UP WITH
ANY.

SO AFTER GIVING IT A
LOT OF THOUGHT I
CONCLUDED IT'S **LESS**
IMPORTANT TO KNOW
THE RIGHT **ANSWERS**
THAN TO BE ABLE TO
PHRASE THE RIGHT
QUESTIONS.

BUT THE ONLY QUESTION
I COULD COME UP WITH
WAS "YOU BUM- WHY
ARE YOU LYING HERE?"

SO I FINALLY SAW THAT THE **ROOT** OF MY PROBLEM LAY NEITHER IN FINDING THE RIGHT ANSWER NOR IN PHRASING THE RIGHT QUESTIONS.

THE ROOT OF MY PROBLEM LAY IN THE **AWARENESS** THAT **IF** THE RIGHT QUESTION **COULD** BE PHRASED, THEN A RIGHT ANSWER UNDOUBTEDLY **MIGHT** BE FOUND.

NOW, KNOWING THIS HAS ALLOWED ME TO **TRANSCEND** THE SHALLOW DILEMMA OF SEEKING ANSWERS OR PHRASING QUESTIONS IN ORDER TO ASSUAGE MY **GUILT.** I KNOW AT **LAST** WHY IT'S **INEVITABLE** THAT I LIE HERE AS I **NOW** LIE!

I'M GROWING.

MR. MERGENDEILER?
THIS IS MR. BLANDLY
OF THE FINK FOUND-
ATION. WE HAVE
RECEIVED YOUR
APPLICATION FOR
AN ENDOWMENT
AND WOULD LIKE
A FEW FURTHER
DETAILS.

AS YOU KNOW MR. MERGEN-
DEILER, THE FINK FOUND-
ATION IS AUTHORIZED TO
GIVE FINANCIAL GRANTS
TO UNWORTHY CAUSES.
CAN YOU PROVE THAT
YOU QUALIFY?

THEN YOU **DO** HAVE REFERENCES.
GOOD. YOUR MOTHER – ALL
YOUR TEACHERS – YOUR
PAST EMPLOYERS. WON-
DERFUL. NO, MR. MERGEN-
DEILER, I DON'T THINK
WE'D NEED THE NAMES
OF GIRL FRIENDS.

NOW, IN THE EVENT YOU **DID** RECEIVE A GRANT, WHAT WOULD YOU DO WITH THE MONEY? I SEE. YOU'D FRITTER IT AWAY. FINE. FINE.

IN WHAT MANNER MAY I ASK? YOU'D LIE IN BED ALL DAY AND READ MYSTERIES. PERFECTLY DELIGHTFUL, MR. MERGEN- DEILER.

ONE LAST QUESTION, MR. MERGENDEILER. IF YOU **WERE** AWARDED A GRANT FOR THIS PROJECT HOW WOULD YOU FEEL? YOU'D FEEL GUILTY. **SPLENDID!**

YOU SHALL RECEIVE YOUR CHECK IN THE MORNING.

SEE THAT GIRL OVER THERE? A **KNOCKOUT?** LOVE TO MEET HER? BEAUTIFUL—QUASI-EXOTIC, BUT WITH **QUALITY?** LISTEN TO ME. **I** KNOW THAT GIRL'S EVERY MOVE BEFORE SHE'LL MAKE IT.

KNOW WHAT SHE'LL ORDER? PERNOD, MAYBE ANISETTE. DURING THE DAY SHE WEARS SEVERE SUITS AND WORKS FOR A PUBLISHER. SHE COMPETES ALL DAY, SO AT NIGHT, LIKE **NOW,** SHE GOES SUPER-FEMININE JUST TO RELAX.

SEE? ANISETTE. EVERY GUY IN THE PLACE HAS HIS EYE ON HER. SHE **KNOWS** IT TOO. LOOKS ALOOF, DOESN'T SHE? BUT WHY COME TO A HANGOUT LIKE THIS IF SHE DOESN'T WANT TO BE PICKED UP? SHE **DOES** WANT TO BE PICKED UP.

BUT SHE'S NERVOUS ABOUT IT. **SEE**
HOW SHE PLAYS WITH THE GLASS?
SHE'S NEVER DONE THIS BEFORE.
PROBABLY JUST BUSTED OFF
WITH HER BOY FRIEND. THEY
WORE EACH OTHER OUT. NOW
SHE WANTS A CHANGE, BUT
ISN'T POSITIVE THAT THIS
IS THE RIGHT WAY TO
FIND IT.

IT DOESN'T **MATTER** NOW. THE
GUY AT THE NEXT TABLE'S
STARTED UP WITH HER. AN ACTOR
TYPE. UNEMPLOYED. HER EX WAS
PROBABLY BOOKISH, SO SHE
OUGHT TO GO FOR THIS. HE
SEEMS OBVIOUS, SO SHE
THINKS HE'LL BE EASY
TO HANDLE. WHAT'D I
TELL YOU? HE'S MOVED
TO HER TABLE. SHE'LL
BE **VERY** DISAPPOINTED.

POOR KID. IF SHE
ONLY KNEW
THAT **I** WHO
UNDERSTAND
WAS
WAITING
HERE ALL
THE
WHILE.

AFTER EIGHT
MONTHS I
STILL
REMEMBER
THE NUMBER.
I WONDER
WHAT THAT
MEANS?

WHO? STEVIE **WHO**?
OH, **THAT** STEVIE!
WELL WHY IN THE WORLD
ARE YOU CALLING ME
AT **THIS** HOUR?

WELL, GOOD FOR **YOU**!
YES, I'M VERY HAPPY
YOU'RE GETTING MARRIED,
BUT MY GOD, FRIEND, I
HAVE TO GO TO **WORK**
TOMORROW!

ALL **RIGHT**, SO YOU'RE NOT
GETTING MARRIED FOR ANOTHER
SIX MONTHS. IT'S YOUR MARRIAGE,
STEVIE, DON'T ASK **MY** OPINION
ON LONG ENGAGEMENTS. LOOK,
I'M **TERRIBLY**
TIRED—

CONGRATULATIONS. I'M **HAPPY**
SHE'S VERY PRETTY. LOOK, I
DON'T HAVE A CIGARET IN THE
HOUSE AND I'M HALF ASLEEP—
CAN YOU CALL ME IN THE
MORNING? ALL **RIGHT**,
SO SHE'S A LOT
PRETTIER THAN
I AM.

STEVIE, IF YOU CALLED TO BE INSULTING I'M GOING TO HANG UP! DID IT EVER OCCUR TO YOU THAT I MIGHT NOT BE CONSIDERED FRIGID BY **EVERY** MAN? SAY, ARE **YOU** DRUNK?

NO, IT'S TOO LATE - NO, THERE'S NO POINT IN YOUR COMING UP. **NO**, STEVIE! I **BELIEVE** YOU'VE WORKED ME OUT OF YOUR SYSTEM. THERE'S REALLY **NO** NEED TO PROVIDE A DEMONSTRATION!

YES, YES. I AGREE. NON-INTELLECTUAL GIRLS ARE **DEFINITELY** BETTER FOR YOU. YES, IT'S GOOD TALKING TO YOU AGAIN **TOO**. NO, I'M BUSY NIGHTS.

OH, ALL RIGHT THEN, LUNCH. YES. NEXT WEEK. **IF** I'M FREE. NOW WITH **YOUR** PERMISSION — YES-YES- **PLEASE** HANG **UP**, STEVIE. I PROMISE. I'LL TRY TO BE FREE. YES. NEXT WEEK. YES. YES. YES-

WHAT HAVE I **DONE**? NOW I'VE GOT **TWO** BROADS CRAZY ABOUT ME.

HELLO HUEY? I WAS
JUST GOING TO HANG
UP. GOD, YOU TAKE
FOREVER TO ANSWER.
ARE YOU ALONE?

NO REASON, I WAS JUST
WONDERING. I **KNOW** IT'S
LATE BUT I GOT A CALL
WAKING **ME** SO I THOUGHT
I'D WAKE **YOU**. DOES THAT
MAKE YOU ANGRY?

NOTHING I DO MAKES YOU ANGRY
DOES IT? YES, I **AM** HOSTILE. WHY
DO **I** ALWAYS HAVE TO CALL **YOU**?
HEY, ARE YOU THERE? ARE YOU
TALKING TO SOMEBODY ELSE?
WELL, WHY IS YOUR HAND OVER
THE PHONE. I
CAN TELL.

NO, DON'T HANG UP! IT'S JUST
THAT I'M VERY DEFENSIVE
WITH YOU. **SAY** WHAT ARE
YOU DOING **RIGHT** NOW?

WELL I THOUGHT MAYBE YOU COULD COME OVER FOR AWHILE. I **KNOW** IT'S LATE BUT-WELL, SURE, IF YOU HAVE A COLD MAYBE IT **ISN'T** A GOOD IDEA TO GO OUT-WELL, I'LL TELL YOU WHAT THEN—

I'LL COME OVER **THERE!** DO YOU HAVE ASPIRINS? IF YOU HAVE A COLD YOU SHOULD DEFINITELY TAKE SOME. I'LL MAKE SOUP, BRING ASPIRIN AND BE OVER IN FIFTEEN MINUTES.

IS THAT LAUGHTER I HEAR IN THE BACKGROUND? YOU **AREN'T** ALONE. I **KNOW** YOU DIDN'T **SAY** YOU WERE. I KNOW — NO, I'M **NOT** HOSTILE. **HONESTLY** I'M NOT.

DON'T HANG UP. LOOK I'LL CALL YOU IN THE MORNING FROM THE OFFICE. NO, NOT TOO EARLY. WELL, WHAT TIME DO YOU THINK YOU'LL BE UP? WELL AFTER LUNCH THEN — WELL, WHAT TIME THEN — ?

AFTER ONE? AFTER TWO? PLEASE DON'T KEEP YOUR HAND OVER THE PHONE — NO, I'M **NOT** HOSTILE — AFTER THREE — ?

SHE'S ALWAYS BEEN
CRAZY ABOUT ME
BUT I DON'T KNOW—
I NEVER THOUGHT
SHE WAS VERY MUCH.

BUT I SEE THE
WAY GUYS LOOK
AT HER ON THE
STREET SO I
GUESS SHE
MUST HAVE A
PRETTY GREAT
FIGURE.

AND I SEE HOW
PEOPLE GATHER
AROUND HER AT
PARTIES SO I
GUESS SHE MUST
HAVE A REALLY
GREAT PERSON-
ALITY.

AND I SEE HOW
HARD EVERYBODY
LISTENS WHEN
SHE TALKS SO I
GUESS SHE MUST
BE EXTREMELY
INTELLIGENT.

 — SO I GUESS I'M
IN LOVE WITH HER.

 — AND I GUESS
I'LL MARRY HER.

 — AND I'LL GUESS
WE'LL BE VERY
HAPPY.

 — SOUNDS LIKE A
VERY GOOD DEAL.

I NEVER USED TO GO OUT ON THE STREET. I WAS ALWAYS AFRAID ID GET BEAT UP.

I KNEW IT WAS A STUPID FEAR. I KNEW IT WAS UNREALISTIC. I LOOKED UP STATISTICS ON PEOPLE WHO GOT BEAT UP WHEN THEY WENT OUT ON THE STREET. IT'S SURPRISINGLY SMALL.

BUT STILL—I HAD MY FOOD DELIVERED. I HAD MY NEWSPAPERS DELIVERED. ALL MY DATES WERE AT **MY** HOUSE. AND AS LONG AS I DIDN'T GO OUT ON THE STREET I SEEMED TO BE FINE.

UNTIL—ONE DAY—I WAS SITTING COMFORTABLY IN MY LIVING ROOM WHEN SUDDENLY IT CAME TO ME THAT I DID NOT **DARE** GO INTO THE KITCHEN—THAT IF I WENT INTO THE KITCHEN I'D GET BEAT UP.

SO I SAT THROUGH ALL FOUR LATE SHOWS THINKING MY PROBLEM OUT. AND AT FIVE IN THE MORNING I FINALLY CONCLUDED THAT IT WASN'T ANYBODY ON THE **OUTSIDE** I WAS AFRAID OF. IT WAS **ME** I WAS AFRAID OF!

THAT ACTUALLY THE ONLY PERSON WHO REGULARLY BEAT ME UP WAS **MYSELF!**

SO I AROSE WITHOUT FEAR AND WENT INTO THE KITCHEN. AND NOBODY BEAT ME UP.

AND I PUT ON MY COAT WITHOUT FEAR AND WENT INTO THE STREET. AND NOBODY BEAT ME UP.

FOR THE FIRST TIME IN YEARS I FELT **ALIVE!** I KNEW I WOULD NEVER BE AFRAID AGAIN!

I FELT SO GOOD THAT THE FIRST COUPLE OF PEOPLE I SAW I BEAT UP.

THERE ARE THREE
OTHER BERNARDS.